Wendy's Great Catch

by Pauline Cartwright
illustrated by Edward Crosby

Harcourt
SCHOOL PUBLISHERS

Printed in China

ISBN 10: 0-15-351384-5
ISBN 13: 978-0-15-351384-8

Ordering Options
ISBN 10: 0-15-351212-1 (Grade 2 Advanced Collection)
ISBN 13: 978-0-15-351212-4 (Grade 2 Advanced Collection)
ISBN 10: 0-15-358044-5 (package of 5)
ISBN 13: 978-0-15-358044-4 (package of 5)

11 12 13 14 15   0940   15 14 13 12 11 10

It had been raining for days, and the Bears were tired of being stuck inside. Finally, the sun came out, so Mom suggested going on a picnic.

"Please can Alvin come along?" asked Bertie, "he's a good friend."

"Yes," answered Dad. "I'll call his mom and ask if it's okay."

When Alvin arrived, the Bears loaded the car and headed for their favorite picnic area. On the way, they stopped to buy some juice.

"I like mango juice," said Bertie.
"I like apple juice," said Wendy.
"I'll get both," said Mom, and
soon they were on their way again.

5

After a while, they came to a police car and a big "STOP" sign.

"The road is still wet and slippery for the next eight miles," said the police officer. "Please drive slowly so you don't have an accident."

BEAR 1

Dad drove very slowly to the picnic area. When they arrived, Bertie and Alvin went to play ball. Mom and Dad got the picnic ready, and Wendy ran after the boys and asked whether she could play, too.

"You are too little," said Bertie.
"I'm good at catching," stated
Wendy, hoping to play.
"Prove it!" said Alvin meanly.

Alvin threw the ball over
Wendy's head, and Bertie caught it.

"That wasn't nice!" said Wendy
angrily to Alvin.

Dad saw Wendy looking glum
and called her to come and eat.

Wendy still wanted to play, but she already knew the answer. She silently ate with Mom and Dad while the boys continued playing. It was hard being a younger sister.

"Come and get a ham sandwich, boys," called Mom.

At that moment, Bertie threw the ball to Alvin, but Alvin missed it. The ball was flying straight for the lunch!

"Look out!" cried Bertie as Wendy leaped up and caught the ball.

"You saved our lunch, Wendy!" said Dad. "That was great timing!"

"Fantastic catch!" called Alvin.

"I told you I was a good catcher,"
Wendy called back proudly.
Bertie grinned at Alvin and said,
"Wendy is better than you!"

13

Alvin and Bertie sat down to eat some ham sandwiches.

"After lunch, let's play ball again," suggested Alvin.

"Only if Wendy can play, too," smiled Bertie.

"It's a deal!" said Wendy happily.

Think Critically

1. Why did the police officer ask Dad to drive slowly?

2. If you were Wendy, how would you have felt when Alvin threw the ball over your head?

3. How can you tell that Dad knew what was going on during the ball game?

4. How did Wendy's feelings about Bertie and Alvin change during the story? How can you tell?

5. When you've been stuck inside because of rain, what is something you like to do when the sun comes out?

⭐ Language Arts

Write a Recount Write a paragraph about a time you went somewhere special with your family. Draw a picture to match.

 School-Home Connection Tell someone at home what happened to Wendy in the story. Make a list of places you would like to visit as a family.

Word Count: 372